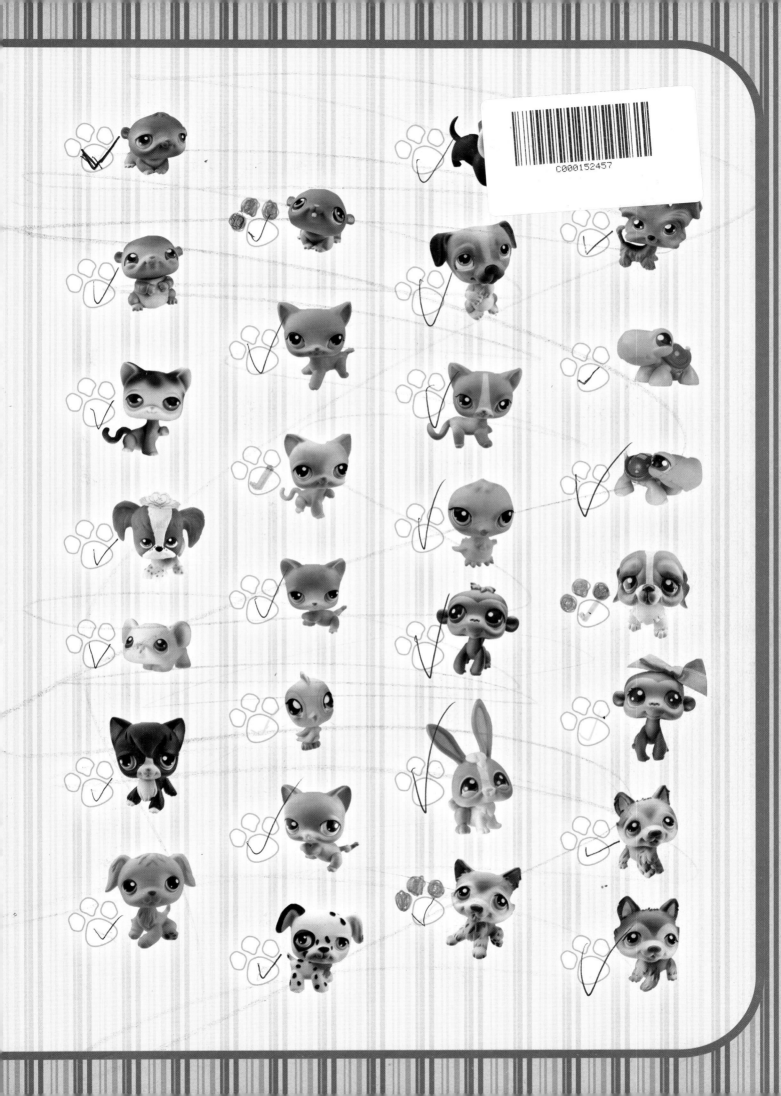

CONTENTS

ANNUAL
2009

Pedigree®

Published 2008. Published by Pedigree Books Limited,
Beech Hill House, Walnut Gardens, Exeter, Devon, EX4 4DH.
Email: books@pedigreegroup.co.uk

£6.99

PLAYTIME PALS

SCOTTIE

Eye Colour: Sky blue
Body Colour: White
Age: 3 ½
Birthday: 10th February
Favourite Accessory: Scottish hat
Loves: Tartan
Pet Peeve: Catty behaviour
Favourite Food: Haggis
Favourite Playtime Game: Chase
Best Friend: Dalmatian

Scottie's full of Highland fun, round lochs and up mountains he loves to run!

"Has anyone seen my bagpipes?"

FERRET

Eye Colour: Periwinkle
Body Colour: White and charcoal
Age: 2
Birthday: 1st September
Favourite Accessory: Pink harness
Loves: Hiding toys
Pet Peeve: Being awake in the day
Favourite Food: Old shoes
Favourite Playtime Game: Hide and seek
Best Friend: Hamster

Ferret's got a cheeky glint in his eye, when he's playing games no rules apply!

"I'm not sneaky... just cleverer than you are!"

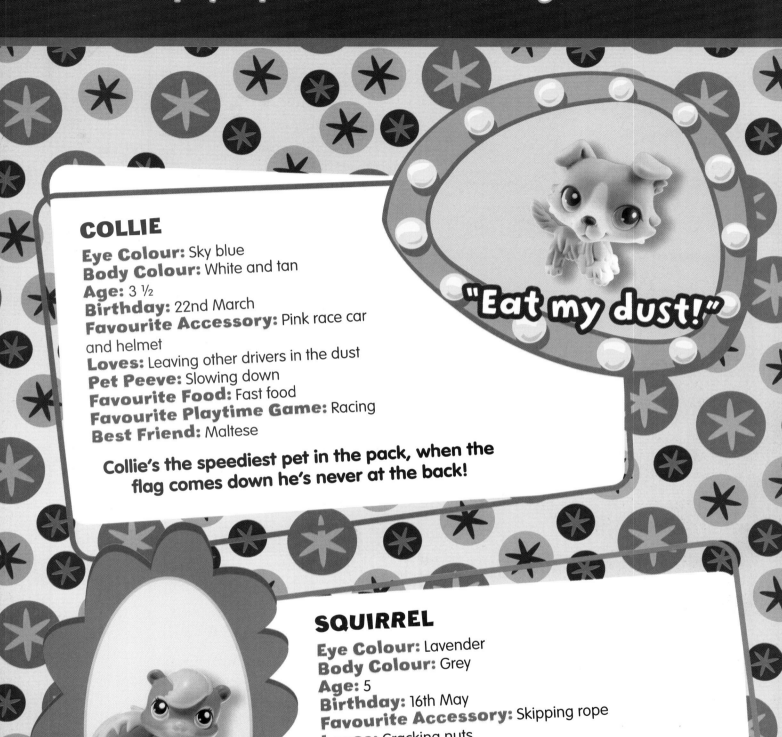

COLLIE

Eye Colour: Sky blue
Body Colour: White and tan
Age: 3 ½
Birthday: 22nd March
Favourite Accessory: Pink race car and helmet
Loves: Leaving other drivers in the dust
Pet Peeve: Slowing down
Favourite Food: Fast food
Favourite Playtime Game: Racing
Best Friend: Maltese

Collie's the speediest pet in the pack, when the flag comes down he's never at the back!

"Eat my dust!"

SQUIRREL

Eye Colour: Lavender
Body Colour: Grey
Age: 5
Birthday: 16th May
Favourite Accessory: Skipping rope
Loves: Cracking nuts
Pet Peeve: Winter
Favourite Food: Pecan pie
Favourite Playtime Game: Hopscotch
Best Friend: Frog

Squirrel hops from tree to tree. The more nuts he can collect the happier he'll be!

"You can never have enough nuts for winter"

DALMATION

Eye Colour: Ice blue
Body Colour: White with black spots
Age: 4
Birthday: 5th August
Favourite Accessory: Red bandanna
Loves: Chasing fire engines
Pet Peeve: Rainy days
Favourite Food: Hot chilli
Favourite Playtime Game: Hot Potato
Best Friend: Scottie

Dalmation loves jumping around, keeping hot and slurping on chilli straight from the pot!

"Which way to the fire station?"

HAMSTER

Eye Colour: Light Blue
Body Colour: Gold and white
Age: 2
Birthday: 24th April
Favourite Accessory: Exercise wheel
Loves: Scampering
Pet Peeve: Standing Still
Favourite Food: Cornflakes
Favourite Playtime Game: Nature trail
Best Friend: Ferret

Hamster likes to keep on the move, simply running in his wheel with nothing to prove!

"I keep running, even if I never get anywhere!"

MOUSE

Eye Colour: Baby blue
Body Colour: Grey
Age: 2 ½
Birthday: 17th November
Favourite Accessory: Anything that can be nibbled
Loves: Secretly scurrying
Pet Peeve: Being bored
Favourite Food: Cheesy chips
Favourite Playtime Game: Building camps
Best Friend: Collie

When Mouse isn't nibbling he's always playing, 'catch me if you can' is what he's saying!

"Got anything to nibble on?"

"Just going for a splash"

FROG

Eye Colour: Light Purple
Body Colour: Aquamarine
Age: 4
Birthday: 9th April
Favourite Accessory: Swimming Goggles
Loves: Splashing
Pet Peeve: Sunbathing
Favourite Food: Lollipops
Favourite Playtime Game: Leap-frog
Best Friend: Squirrel

Frog loves nothing more than splashing around, he's always in the water, never on the ground!

TOTALLY TALENTED

"I want a rematch"

BULLDOG

Eye Colour: Chocolate brown
Body Colour: Light brown and white
Age: 4
Birthday: 13th July
Favourite Accessory: Board games

Loves: Playing British bulldog
Pet Peeve: Losing
Favourite Food: T-Bone steak
Top Talent: Winning
Best Friend: Kitten

Bulldog's competitive nature is fun, as long as he is always number one!

KITTEN

Eye Colour: Baby blue
Body Colour: Gold and white
Age: 3
Birthday: 30th January
Favourite Accessory: Trainers

Loves: Joining in
Pet Peeve: Heights
Favourite Food: Tuna toastie
Top Talent: Playing tag
Best Friend: Bulldog

Kitten is full of tricks and fast, when it comes to games he's never last!

"Tag! You're it!"

HORSE

Eye Colour: Pale blue
Body Colour: Gold and white
Age: 4
Birthday: 2nd May
Favourite Accessory: Pink Saddle

Loves: Prancing
Pet Peeve: Surprises
Favourite Food: Sugar cubes
Top Talent: Show-jumping
Best Friend: Bunny

Horse can learn any trick, not only is she clever but also quick!

"I'm not a one-trick pony!"

These cute and cuddly pets are the cleverest kind. They love to learn tricks so get teaching them quick!

GECKO

Eye Colour: Olive and brown
Body Colour: Green with orange spots
Age: 2 ½
Birthday: 20th August
Favourite Accessory: Necklace

Loves: Hiding
Pet Peeve: Being Found
Favourite Food: Chinese
Top Talent: Changing colours
Best Friend: Owl

Gecko's a master of hide and seek, but if you're his friend he might let you peek!

"Now you see me, now you don't!"

"Take it to the max, dude!"

BUNNY

Eye Colour: Light blue
Body Colour: Chocolate brown and white
Age: 3
Birthday: 4th January
Favourite Accessory: Skateboard

Loves: Extreme sports
Pet Peeve: Laziness
Favourite Food: Energy bars
Top Talent: Doing back-flips
Best Friend: Horse

Bunny's the most daring pet of them all, be it back-flips, triple-dives or free-fall!

OWL

Eye Colour: Yellow-brown
Body Colour: Gold and tan
Age: 5
Birthday: 31st October
Favourite Accessory: Moonlight

Loves: Hooting
Pet Peeve: Early mornings
Favourite Food: Midnight feasts
Top Talent: Flying at night
Best Friend: Gecko

At night time Owl takes lots of pleasure, flying and hooting entirely at his leisure!

"Is it night time yet?"

SQUEAKY CLEAN

Whether they're splashing in the bath or checking the Doggie Diner's spotless, these pets love to stay clean and fresh!

"Order's up!"

JACK RUSSELL TERRIER

Eye Colour: Warm brown
Body Colour: Golden brown, dark brown and white
Age: 5
Birthday: 25th July
Favourite Accessory: Chef's hat

Loves: Running the Doggie Diner
Pet Peeve: Burnt toast
Favourite Food: Bacon cheeseburgers
Best Friend: Golden Retriever

Jack Russell Terrier likes nothing finer than cooking and cleaning in his special Doggie Diner!

FISH

Eye Colour: Yellow-green
Body Colour: Orange with white stripes
Age: 3
Birthday: 10th November
Favourite Accessory: Aquarium

Loves: Blowing bubbles
Pet Peeve: Sharks
Favourite Food: Sushi
Best Friend: Duck

Fish can usually be found swimming laps or munching on cucumber sushi perhaps!

"Splish splash I was taking a bath"

DUCK

Eye Colour: Aquamarine
Body Colour: Yellow and orange
Age: 4
Birthday: 2nd May
Favourite Accessory: Fluffy beach towel

Loves: Bathing
Pet Peeve: Ruffled feathers
Favourite Food: Vanilla ice cream
Best Friend: Fish

Duck loves his feathers getting nice and wet and after a rub in his fluffy towel he really is the cutest pet!

"Anyone for a swim?"

AQUARIUM FRIENDS

Whether they're playing on the sand or paddling in the sea, these colourful critters are always ready to splash the day away on the beach...but don't forget the suntan lotion!

IGUANA

Eye Colour: Orange and brown
Body Colour: Light green
Age: 4
Birthday: 14th June
Favourite Accessory: Sunglasses
Loves: Lying on sunlit rocks

Pet Peeve: Sunburns
Favourite Food: Sun-dried tomatoes
Favourite Beach Game: Bat and ball
Best Friend: Turtle

When Iguana's not soaking up the sun, he's making friends on the beach for plenty of fun!

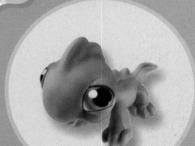

"Reptiles rule!"

"Surf's up!"

HERMIT CRAB

Eye Colour: Neon green
Body Colour: Pink
Age: 6
Birthday: 10th September
Favourite Accessory: MP3 Player
Loves: Surfer music
Pet Peeve: Big waves

Favourite Food: Fish and chips
Favourite Beach Game: Rock-pooling
Best Friend: Iguana

Hermit Crab is the coolest on the sand, when the sun's out he always has a party planned!

TURTLE

Eye Colour: Dark turquoise
Body Colour: Pea green
Age: 3
Birthday: 17th December
Favourite Accessory: Backpack
Loves: Travelling
Pet Peeve: Traffic jams

Favourite Food: Beach picnic
Favourite Beach Game: Building sandcastles
Best Friend: Crab

Turtle can't wait for that time of year, when the sun comes out and the clouds disappear!

"Hooray for holidays!"

PET MIX UP!

Can you unscramble each word to discover the names of the Littlest Pet Shop pets below? Then draw a line to the picture to match the pet to their name.

1. LODOEP

2. DULBIERB

3. UGP

PUG

4. TAC

5. TELURT

6. SEOMU

14

CRAZY MAZE!

Can you help these Polar Puppies find their little lost friend in the giant snowball?

CROSSWORD TIME

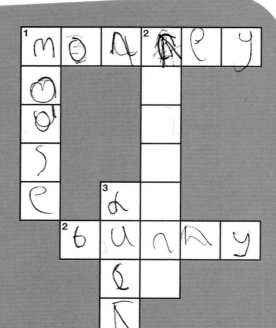

ACROSS

1. A pet that loves bananas
2. A pet that loves to hop

DOWN

1. The littlest pet of all
2. The Curious_____
3. A pet who loves to swim and quack

ACROSS

1. A pet who loves to run but not go far
2. A very Scottish dog

DOWN

1. A pet you can ride
2. A pet who meows
3. A green pet with a hard shell

WHAT'S THE DIFFERENCE?

These pets are totally twins but if you look closely all is not the same! Look at the top picture and then look at the bottom picture. Can you spot ten differences? Look carefully and circle the ones you see...

BEST FRIENDS

What makes a best friend?
Best friends come in all shapes and sizes, you may not look the same on the outside but on the inside best friends have a lot in common. Your best friend is your closest pal. You spend the most time with them and think about them a lot when they're not with you.
"The great thing about a best friend is having someone to play with," says Cat.
It could be at the park or the fun fair, it doesn't matter what you do as long as you're together!

Maybe your best friend doesn't live near you or has moved far away? Don't worry, you can still talk to them and hear from them. Best friends always find a way to keep in touch, even if they're not in the same place.
It might be a quick phone call or a long letter. It only takes a minute to send an email telling her you miss her or to draw him a funny picture of the two of you having fun.
Whatever effort you make to keep in touch it's worth it just to imagine the smile and happy feeling you'll give them all day long!

What kind of fun do you have with your best friend?

Maybe you ride bicycles in the garden or race on skateboards together in the park? Whatever you enjoy the most, it's always more fun with your best friend than on your own.

Perhaps you walk to school together or play 'I Spy' in the backseat of the car on the way into town?

"Wherever you're going, if your best friend's with you, it makes getting there all the more fun!" says Bunny.

Best friends make doing any activity twice the fun! When you're shopping together you can help each other choose what to wear or eat. If you like the same toys you see, there's no need to buy one each. One of the greatest things about friendship is sharing. Your best friend will always want to share their toys or swap games with you.

If your doggy bag is a little low on pocket money, pressing your nose against the shop glass and picking out what you like is lots of fun. Try window-shopping with your best friend and see how much you laugh together!

"Just being with a friend is better than anything money can buy!" says Poodle.

When it's your birthday your best friend will always be there to celebrate with you.

Duck wishes Frog a very happy birthday by singing to him. "Happy birthday to you, happy birthday to you, happy birthday dear Frog, happy birthday to you!" Frog is delighted that his best friend has made his day even more special.

Birthday parties are great for spending time with friends and family but your best friend is the one who will help you choose which party games and tunes to play to make sure you have a fantastic time. They might even buy you the biggest present!

The Twin Turtles are lucky enough to share the same birthday with their best friend; each other!

Best friends always have something to celebrate, whether it's a birthday or a holiday or just being together.

When the school term's ended and the sunshine appears, it must be the long summer holidays!

Holidays are a great chance to spend lots of time with your best friend. You could ask your parents to help you plan a special day with your best friend.

In their summer holidays, Mouse and Turtle like to go to the beach together. Sometimes they'll build sandcastles or paddle in the sea, but whatever they do, Turtle says, "We always have loads of fun in the sun!"

You could even have your best friend to stay.

Having a sleepover is great fun. You and your best friend get to stay up late in your pyjamas sharing snacks and secrets.

Poodle and Bunny can't help but giggle together as they have pillow fights and paint their toenails before snuggling into their sleeping bags to watch a film.

Being with your best friend is always a treat and sometimes they need to hear how special they are to you.

Sometimes your best friend might be having a bad day or feeling a little sad. It's your duty as their best friend to make them feel better. Let them know they're special by treating them to something they love.

Your best friend might love to receive a friendship bracelet or you could take them to a café to share a yummy chocolate cake.

When Kitty's feeling down, Iguana usually takes her to the playground. "The bumpy slide always makes her laugh and smile again," says Iguana. Best friends like each other just the way they are but it's sometimes fun to play at pretending you're different by giving each other a makeover!

You can each find a "purr-fect" new look by getting out old dressing up clothes or trying on each other's sparkly jewellery. You could swap a necklace for a hair bow or even a hat.

Poodle loves to dress like a grown-up in a pretty hat, topped off with a pink flower clip! One thing's for sure, Cat knows having her best friend by her side is always her best accessory!

Your best friend is your best supporter!
When you're playing games in the park or joining in with school sports' day, your best friend is guaranteed to be there cheering you on.
Even when you're tired or feeling a little slow and unsure you can make it, your best friend will call out your name and spur you on.

Then when you win you can share your prize with your best friend to say thank you for helping you believe in yourself.
On sports' day, Pug makes sure he's always there for Turtle, giving him an extra boost as he nears the finishing line, "Go Turtle, go!!"

Best friends are never stuck for fun things to do together come rain or shine.
When the sun's out and it's a hot day, a best friend picnic is a great way to enjoy the weather together. The Littlest Pet Shop pets like to find a shady spot, add a blanket and, most important of all, they bring a basket full of yummy treats to share like

chocolate cakes or ice lollies!
In fact it doesn't matter if you don't like the same goodies. Pig likes to eat cheese sandwiches and Cat prefers to munch on sardines but they both enjoy watching pets playing in the park and spending the afternoon looking for weird cloud shapes in the sky.

When winter's on the way and it's chilly outside, best friends can have just as much fun together.

It's always best to make sure yourself and your best friend are wrapped up snug and warm before you head outside to play in the cold.

A best friend will always help their winter pal with their woolly hat, scarf and mittens.

Once out in the snow your best friend can help you make a snowman or even a snow-pet! Using a carrot for a nose and some sticks and stones to make eyes and a smiley mouth, you can create life-size snowmen with funny faces to make each other laugh. Bunny and Mouse just managed to finish theirs before the snow started to melt!

Some of the pets prefer to ice-skate or ride down hill on a speedy sledge! You definitely need your best friend for this as it's much faster with two!

Mealtimes are often a good time to spend together with your best friend.

Whether it's going to your best friend's house for dinner or having a picnic on the beach, snacks always taste better when you share them. Your best friend will always be the one who offers you a crisp from their packet or their last sweet in the bag.

Sharing your food with your best friend is always kind and thoughtful and a way of letting them know how special they are. It's part of what makes friendship so yummy!

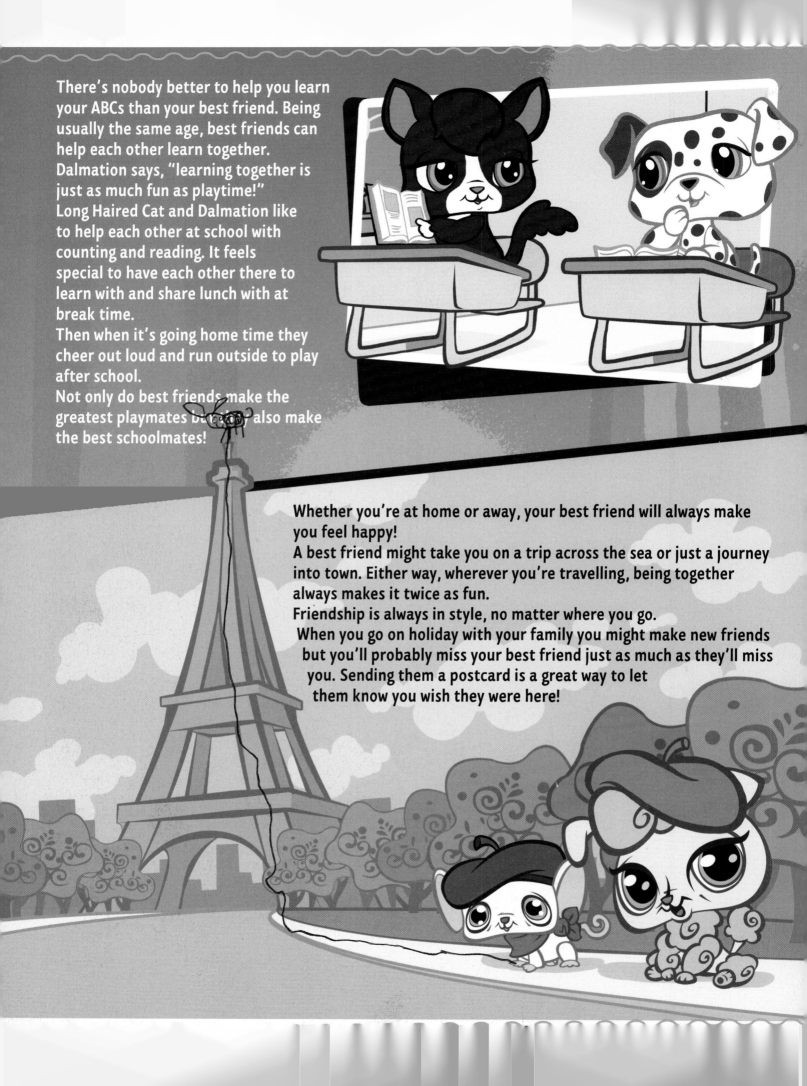

There's nobody better to help you learn your ABCs than your best friend. Being usually the same age, best friends can help each other learn together. Dalmation says, "learning together is just as much fun as playtime!"
Long Haired Cat and Dalmation like to help each other at school with counting and reading. It feels special to have each other there to learn with and share lunch with at break time.
Then when it's going home time they cheer out loud and run outside to play after school.
Not only do best friends make the greatest playmates but they also make the best schoolmates!

Whether you're at home or away, your best friend will always make you feel happy!
A best friend might take you on a trip across the sea or just a journey into town. Either way, wherever you're travelling, being together always makes it twice as fun.
Friendship is always in style, no matter where you go.
When you go on holiday with your family you might make new friends but you'll probably miss your best friend just as much as they'll miss you. Sending them a postcard is a great way to let them know you wish they were here!

Best friends can do a million fun things together!
As well as playing games you could get creative together. Like the Littlest Pet Shop Pets you could paint pictures or dance and play music together.
Or maybe your best friend likes to cook and you can help them bake fairy cakes?
Or perhaps you like to put on plays with your best friend for the grown-ups or snap pictures of each other? Everyone likes to do different activities and find their own way of having fun but the greatest thing about having a best friend means you can do these things together.

SHARE THE FUN!

Best friends are always there for each other, through good times and bad. As well as playing and having fun with your best friend they can help you do the things in life that take two, like going up and down on a see-saw. The Twin Monkeys like to ride a tandem bicycle together. They know they couldn't get very far on their own. Sharing with your best friend always helps you do more!
You can always find a best friend at the Littlest Pet Shop who'll be there to hug you and remind you how special you are to them.
"Everything's more fun when you share it with a best friend!" says Bird.

SUPER SASSY

Be it living it up or taking it easy, these kitties know what they want... but more than anything they want your love!

TABBY CAT

Eye Colour: Yellow-green
Body Colour: Gold, white and dark brown
Age: 3
Birthday: 27th April
Favourite Accessory: Hairbrush
Loves: Being pampered
Pet Peeve: Swimming
Favourite Food: Honeycomb ice cream
Perfect pleasure: Stroking
Best Friend: Persian Cat

Tabby Cat loves stroking and grooming, and lying in the garden next to flowers blooming!

"How do I look in this?"

PERSIAN CAT

Eye Colour: Ice blue
Body Colour: Cream, gold and dark brown
Age: 4
Birthday: 4th October
Favourite Accessory: Hair ribbon
Loves: Lazy afternoons on the sofa
Pet Peeve: Aerobics
Favourite Food: Prawn cocktail
Perfect pleasure: Sleeping
Best Friend: Tabby Cat

When Persian Cat isn't preening her hair, she's relaxing and dozing in a comfy chair!

"Would you be a dear and brush out my tangles?'

CURIOUS KITTIES

The Curious Kitties are three of a kind, if you stroke them and groom them their love you'll find!

CURIOUS KITTIE

Eye Colour: Sky blue
Body Colour: Gold and white
Age: 2
Birthday: 6th March
Favourite Accessory: Catnip toy

Loves: Feather beds
Pet Peeve: Waking up early
Favourite Food: Sweet chilli prawns
Perfect pleasure: Purring
Best Friend: Curious Kitties

"Meow!"

"Who wants to go to the salon?"

CURIOUS KITTIE

Eye Colour: Grassy-green
Body Colour: White and orange
Age: 2
Birthday: 6th March
Favourite Accessory: Key-ring charm

Loves: Getting toenails painted
Pet Peeve: Split ends
Favourite Food: Salmon sushi
Perfect pleasure: Head massage
Best Friend: Curious Kitties

CURIOUS KITTIE

Eye Colour: Emerald green
Body Colour: Gold and white
Age: 2
Birthday: 6th March
Favourite Accessory: Sleeping mask

Loves: Scratching posts
Pet Peeve: Hairballs
Favourite Food: Tuna sushi
Perfect pleasure: Licking paws
Best Friend: Curious Kitties

"Is it time for my cat nap?"

PRIM 'N' PROPER

SIAMESE CAT

Eye Colour: Sapphire blue
Body Colour:
White and charcoal
Age: 4
Birthday: 12th November
Favourite Accessory: Tiara

Loves: Anything sparkly
Pet Peeve: Not looking her best
Favourite Food: Caviar
Best Friend: Long Haired Cat

Siamese Cat loves to sparkle and shine, and only on the finest foods she'll dine!

"Diamonds are a cat's best friend"

SHIH TZU

Eye Colour: Dark blue
Body Colour:
Gold, brown and dark brown
Age: 3
Birthday: 25th February
Favourite Accessory:
Hair bow

Loves: Prancing around
Pet Peeve:
Disorganised wardrobes
Favourite Food:
Strawberry mousse
Best Friend: Fish

Shih tzu always has to look his best, putting his cute looks and long hair to the test!

"Who wants to go shopping?"

LONG HAIRED CAT

Eye Colour: Crystal blue
Body Colour: White
Age: 2
Birthday: 30th September
Favourite Accessory:
Chopsticks

Loves: Karate
Pet Peeve: Using a fork
Favourite Food:
Anything Chinese
Best Friend: Siamese Cat

Long Haired Cat loves all things Chinese, give her noodles or kung fu and she's easy to please!

"Hi-ya!"

With a passion for fashion, these pets know how to accessorise and when to get their beauty sleep. Give them plenty of cuddles and you can be the same!

FISH

Eye Colour: Ocean blue
Body Colour: Yellow
Age: 3
Birthday: 2nd July
Favourite Accessory: Water

Loves: Collecting seashells
Pet Peeve: Rocks
Favourite Food: Crispy seaweed
Best Friend: Shih tzu

When Fish isn't swimming in the sea she's preening her fins, usually before the day begins!

"Who wants to go for a dip?"

"I'd rather be napping"

PERSIAN CAT

Eye Colour: Light green
Body Colour: White
Age: 4
Birthday: 16th May
Favourite Accessory: Comfy cat bed

Loves: Lounging around
Pet Peeve: Going to the gym
Favourite Food: Banana pudding
Best Friend: Long Haired Cat

Persian Cat would rather be lazing around, than rushing or fussing or making a sound!

COCKATOO

Eye Colour: Pale blue
Body Colour: White and yellow
Age: 3
Birthday: 13th March
Favourite Accessory: Compact mirror
Loves: Chatting on the phone

Pet Peeve: Being away from friends
Favourite Food: Apple pie
Best Friend: Blue bird

Cockatoo is a sociable little critter, on the phone to her friends you can hear her gossip and titter!

"I'm a pretty bird"

PRIM 'N' PROPER

"Does my outfit match?"

CALICO CAT

Eye Colour: Grassy green
Body Colour:
Gold, white and charcoal
Age: 4
Birthday: 26th January
Favourite Accessory:
Butterfly cat toy

Loves: Jumping
Pet Peeve: Rainy days
Favourite Food: Cheeries
Best Friend: Kitten

Calico Cat is a lively sort, being fast and graceful he never gets caught

KITTEN

Eye Colour: Light blue
Body Colour: Gold and white
Age: 4
Birthday: 19th August
Favourite Accessory:
Hair dryer

Loves:
Reading gossip magazines
Pet Peeve: Nail clippers
Favourite Food: Japanese
Best Friend: Calico Cat

Kitten loves nothing more than doing her hair, and then lapping up the fuss as people adoringly stare!

"Don't I look purr-fect?"

"I love to keep my feathers soft"

BLUE BIRD

Eye Colour: Blue-green
Body Colour: Turquoise
Age: 2
Birthday: 21st September
Favourite Accessory:
Perch

Loves: Getting her nails clipped
Pet Peeve: Untidy nails
Favourite Food:
Sunflower seeds
Best Friend: Cockatoo

Blue bird is a pretty little creature, who after preening and cleaning will always feature!

POODLE

Eye Colour: Light blue
Body Colour: Light pink
Age: 4
Birthday: 29th July
Favourite Accessory:
Magic wand

Loves:
Going to the hairdressers for perms
Pet Peeve: Frizzy hair
Favourite Food: Candy floss
Best Friend: Bunny

When Poodle isn't perming her hair into curls, many a magic trick she unfurls!

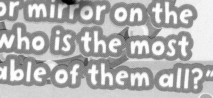

"Watch me make this rabbit disappear"

"That's magic!"

BUNNY

Eye Colour: Light blue
Body Colour: Snow white
Age: 3
Birthday: 12th May
Favourite Accessory:
Magic hat

Loves: Vanishing
Pet Peeve: Reappearing
Favourite Food:
Carrot cake
Best Friend: Poodle

Bunny loves using her magic hat, muttering magic words she can even produce a cat!

KITTY

Eye Colour: Light blue
Body Colour:
Grey and charcoal
Age: 2
Birthday: 4th December
Favourite Accessory:
Sparkly jewellery
Loves: Preening

Pet Peeve: Being rushed
Favourite Food:
Chocolate biscuits
Best Friend: Cat

When Kitty sees a mirror on the wall, looking at herself, in love she'll fall!

"Mirror mirror on the wall, who is the most fashionable of them all?"

Dog Days

BEAGLE

Eye Colour: Honey-brown
Body Colour: Golden brown
Age: 4
Birthday: 4th January
Favourite Accessory: Teddy bear
Loves: Being spoiled
Pet Peeve: Cooking
Favourite Food: Take-away food
Best Dog Trick: Jumping
Best Friend: Poodle

Beagle is full of life and non-stop fun and when he's out in the park, he'll run, run and run!

"Heard any good gossip?"

POODLE

Eye Colour: Pale blue
Body Colour: White
Age: 2
Birthday: 9th June
Favourite Accessory: Flower hair clip
Loves: Hugs and kisses
Pet Peeve: Rude behaviour
Favourite Food: French fries
Best Dog Trick: Lie down
Best Friend: Beagle

Poodle is one classy doggie, he's got taste and style and will never chase a moggie!

"Bonjour!"

These are the loyalist friends you'll find and with lots of squeaky toys and doggie biscuits every day can be a dog day!

CHIHUAHUA

Eye Colour: Chocolate brown
Body Colour: Cream and light brown
Age: 3
Birthday: 27th November
Favourite Accessory: Chew toy
Loves: Trips to Mexico
Pet Peeve: Being cold
Favourite Food: Mexican food
Best Dog Trick: Back flip
Best Friend: Pug

Chihuahua is one hot dog with spicy taste, if there's a burrito around it won't go to waste!

"Can I borrow your jumper?"

PUG

Eye Colour: Brown-green
Body Colour: Light and dark brown
Age: 2
Birthday: 14th February
Favourite Accessory: Romance novels
Loves: Long walks on the beach
Pet Peeve: Stormy weather
Favourite Food: Anything by candlelight
Best Dog Trick: Heek
Best Friend: Chihuahua

Pug is a lover not a fighter and when he loves you, no other pet could hug you tighter!

"I'm such a romantic!"

Dog Days

SCOTTIE

Eye Colour: Emerald green
Body Colour: Black
Age: 4
Birthday: 12th September
Favourite Accessory: Kilt
Loves: Fashion magazines
Pet Peeve: Wearing stripes
Favourite Food: Cappuccino
Best Dog Trick: Fetch
Best Friend: Boxer

Scottie's favourite dog days involve taking the lead, in fashion and style rather than speed!

"I've got my stylist on speed dial"

"Let's be friends"

BOXER

Eye Colour: Honey brown
Body Colour: White and brown
Age: 3
Birthday: 7th October
Favourite Accessory: Fire hydrant toy
Loves: Going for walks
Pet Peeve: Bad tempers
Favourite Food: Anything that can be shared
Best Dog Trick: Play dead
Best Friend: Scottie

When Boxer's around you'll never feel alone, he's bound to share his juicy bone!

COCKER SPANIEL

Eye Colour: Warm brown
Body Colour: Cream and gold
Age: 5
Birthday: 30th September
Favourite Accessory: Purple tiara
Loves: Singing in the shower
Pet Peeve: Being off-key
Favourite Food: Hot tea with lemon
Best Dog Trick: Singing along with music
Best Friend: German Shepherd

Cocker Spaniel loves nothing more than a tuneful song, she'll tell you her voice is beautiful and she's definitely not wrong!

"I should've been a professional singer"

"I'll protect you!"

GERMAN SHEPHERD

Eye Colour: Light brown
Body Colour: Golden brown
Age: 4
Birthday: 1st December
Favourite Accessory: Torch
Loves: Staying up late
Pet Peeve: Strangers
Favourite Food: Strong coffee
Best Dog Trick: Guarding the pet shop
Best Friend: Cocker Spaniel

German Shepherd is a brave dog who'll protect you till the end, but he'll also be your bestest friend!

PLAYFUL PUPPIES

The Playful Puppies will keep you busy all day, but be warned you'll need boundless energy to be able to play!

"Lets go to the dog park"

PLAYFUL PUPPY

Eye Colour: Lavender
Body Colour: Cocoa brown and white
Age: 1
Birthday: 18th July
Favourite Accessory: Anything he can fetch

Loves: Running around with friends
Pet Peeve: Being alone
Favourite Food: Peanut butter
Best Dog Trick: Licking faces
Best Friend: Playful Puppies

PLAYFUL PUPPY

Eye Colour: Lavender
Body Colour: Golden brown and white
Age: 1
Birthday: 18th July
Favourite Accessory: The telephone

Loves: Telling jokes
Pet Peeve: Being told to be quiet
Favourite Food: Chicken nuggets
Best Dog Trick: Being funny
Best Friend: Playful Puppies

"Did you hear the one about..."

"I'm just gonna take a quick nap"

PLAYFUL PUPPY

Eye Colour: Lavender
Body Colour: Cocoa brown
Age: 1
Birthday: 18th July
Favourite Accessory: A cosy blanket

Loves: taking naps
Pet Peeve: Alarm clocks
Favourite Food: Hot chocolate
Best Dog Trick: Lying down
Best Friend: Playful P uppies

TOTALLY TWINS

Double the fun and double the trouble, these lucky pets get up to all kinds of fun with each other. Imagine having your best friend with you all the time!

TWIN KITTENS

Eye Colour: Bright blue
Body Colour: White
Eye Colour: Sky blue
Body Colour: White and orange
Age: 3
Birthday: 14th January

Favourite Accessories: Each other
Loves: Cuddling
Pet Peeve: Water fights
Favourite Food: Sardines
Best Friend: Twin Kittens

Twin Kittens are cuddly and love to share, when snuggled up together they really are a cute pair!

"We need a good home!"

TWIN TURTLES

Eye Colour: Brown
Body Colour: Green with brown spotted shell
Eye Colour: Brown
Body Colour: Green with pink spotted shell
Age: 2
Birthday: 8th May

Favourite Accessories: Suave sunglasses
Loves: Moving slowly
Pet Peeve: Minimum speed limites
Favourite Food: Crab sticks
Best Friend: Twin Turtles

Twin Turtles are great companions and always go slow, but luckily they've never got far to go!

"Are we there yet?"

TWIN MONKEYS

Eye Colour: Purple
Body Colour: Golden and brown
Eye Colour: Jungle green
Body Colour: Tan and cocoa
Age: 2
Birthday: 26th July

Favourite Accessories: Vines to swing from
Loves: Swinging
Pet Peeve: Being apart
Favourite Food: Banana split (with two spoons)
Best Friend: Twin Monkeys

The cheeky Twin Monkeys love to swing and as they cling to the vines they also sing!

"Wanna hang out?"

Make a
Friendship Bracelet

You will need six different coloured pieces of embroidery thread to begin…

1) Cut the threads all to the same size – approximately 60 cm each. Gather the six ends of the threads together and tie in a knot at the top. Arrange them in the order you would like for your best friend's bracelet. Stick the knotted end to something firm like a table or chair.

1 2 3 4 5 6

2) Take strand 1 and wrap it over and around strand 2 to make a knot. Tighten by holding strand 2 and pulling up on strand 1.

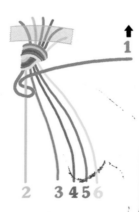

2 3 4 5 6

3) Tie a second knot in the same way by knotting strand 1 over and around strand 2 again. Pull up on strand 1 as before and tighten.

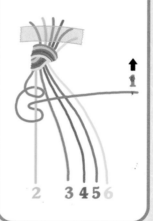

2 3 4 5 6

4) Leave strand 2 and pick up strand 3. Tie two knots with strand 1 by wrapping it over and around strand 3, in the same way you did with strand 2.

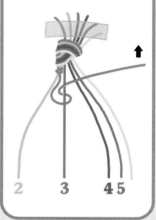

2 3 4 5

5) Repeat these steps on strands 4, 5 and 6 by tying two knots on each with strand 1. Now strand 1 will be on the right and you have completed one row!

2 3 4 5 6 1

6) Start the next row by taking strand 2 and tying two knots over and around strands 3, 4, 5, 6 and 1.

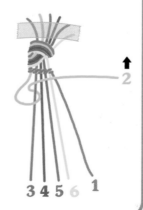

3 4 5 6 1

7) When you have finished enough rows to fit around your wrist, tie another knot to complete bracelet. When you give the bracelet to your best friend, tie the two ends together around their wrist and trim off the extra thread to make a perfect fit!

3 4 5 6 1

1 2 3 4 5 6

Help Kitten

Can you help Kitten find her ball of wool?

1   2   3

Which Pet is the PURR-FECT Match for You?

Pets have different personalities just like you and your friends do. When you choose a pet who's going to be your best friend forever it helps to pick one that likes to do the same things as you and suits your personality perfectly.

Try this quiz to seek out the pet that matches you the most. Just tick the answer that best describes you, add up the amount of 'a,b,c & d's you have and see below to discover the type of pet that suits you best!

1. These words best describe me:
A) Active and Playful ....
B) Quiet and shy ....
C) Warm and friendly ....
D) Outgoing and exciting ....

2. I like to spend the weekend:
A) At the park, the beach or going for walks.........
B) Reading a good book ....
C) Laughing and joking with a best friend ....
D) Learning new and exciting things ....

3. My dream holiday would be:
A) Camping under the stars ....
B) Lying on a sunny beach ....
C) Going to an amusement park ....
D) Exploring a tropical island ....

4. My favourite clothes are:
A) Sporty and fun ....
B) Designer ....
C) Anything comfortable ....
D) Brightly coloured..............................

5. Some of my favourite colours are:
A) Blue and red...................................
B) Pink and purple................................
C) Orange and yellow ....
D) Bright green and aquamarine....................

6. When I grow up I want to be:
A) An athlete......................................
B) A film star ....
C) A clown ....
D) An astronaut ....

...Mostly A's; a playful puppy is the perfect pet to match your fun and active life. You'll have a fantastic time enjoying the great outdoors together!

...Mostly B's; a sweet little kitten or cat is your best match as they will love curling up with you for quiet time and hours of pampering!

...Mostly C's; a funny mouse will keep you giggling for hours. You and everyone you know can enjoy laughing together as he entertains you!

...Mostly D's; Just as you like to be outgoing and adventurous, so does an exotic bird. Pick one of these and you can explore the exciting world together!

Your Best Friend and You!

My Profile

My name **Scarlett**

My eye colour **greeny blue**

My birthday **May the 20**

My favourite accessory **Boots**

Likes

Pet Peeve

My favourite food

My favourite game

My Best Friend's Profile

Name

Eye colour

Birthday

Favourite accessory

Likes

Pet Peeve

Favourite food

Favourite game

Just as the Littlest Pet Shop pets have their own profiles, so do you and your best friend. Your personality is unique but you will like a lot of the same things as your best friend – that's what makes you get on so well! Fill in yours and your Best Friend's profile to see how much you have in common.

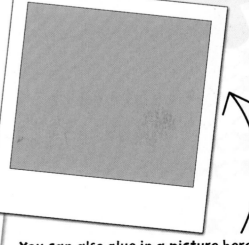

You can also glue in a picture here of you and your best friend or if you don't have one you can draw one of the two of you together!

Doggie Diner Recipes!

Here are some of Jack Russell Terrier's favourite recipes. He loves cooking for his friends and so will you! Always remember to ask an adult for help with cooking.

CHOCOLATE CORNFLAKE CAKES

Here's what you'll need:
- 50g of Butter
- 4 tbsp of Golden Syrup
- 100g of Plain or Milk Chocolate
- 75g of Cornflakes
- 15 Fairy cake cases

How to make the cakes:

STEP 1
First ask an adult for help in the kitchen.

STEP 2
Use scales to measure all the ingredients.

STEP 3
In a small saucepan, gently melt the butter, golden syrup and chocolate until it's runny.

STEP 4
Stir in the cornflakes.

STEP 5
Place large spoonfuls of the mixture in fairy cake cases and place on a tray.

STEP 6
Leave to set in the fridge for 2 hours.

LITTLEST PET SHOP CUP CAKES

Here's what you'll need:
- 2 Large Eggs, cracked open
- 1 tsp of Vanilla Essence
- 125g of Caster Sugar
- 125g of Soft Margarine
- 125g of Self-raising Flour
- Fairy cake cases

To decorate you can use:
- Tubes of writing icing
- Marshmallows (big and small)
- Food Colouring
- Small coloured sweets

How to make the cakes:

STEP 1
Heat the oven to 180C/350F/Gas 4. Put all the ingredients in a bowl and beat them together until the mixture is smooth and slightly lighter in colour.

STEP 2
Line a baking tray with fairy cake cases and half-fill each case with the mixture.

STEP 3
Cook the cakes for 18-20 minutes. You can tell they're done when they have risen up and are a golden colour.

STEP 4
The cupcakes can be decorated using icing spread over the top of the cake, marshmallows, writing icing, food colouring and coloured sweets. To make pet shop pets, try decorating the cakes with the Littlest Pet Shop pets' faces. Use pink food colouring and 2 marshmallows for Hermit Crab and green food colouring and white sweets for Frog, etc...

Totally Talented Pets

"Welcome to the show!" announces St. Bernard. Like people, the Littlest Pet Shop Pets have lots of talents. There are as many talents as there are stars in the night sky.

Do you have a talent? Maybe you're a star singer or a brilliant gymnast?

Or you may not have discovered your talent yet, but if there's something you've always dreamed of doing, why not give it a try?

Check out these totally talented pets! Do they share any of your talents?

Hamster is an expert juggler because she's quick with her hands.

When she's performing, the balls fly through the air with ease. Can she catch them all?

"The trick is to not take your eye off the balls!" says Hamster.

Having eight arms makes juggling a little easier for Spider!

She can juggle more than just balls. After a day at the beach she's collected some rather different items to show off her juggling skills!

"I like to juggle with anything I can get my many arms on," says Spider.

Are you ready to rock 'n' roll? These friends love to play music together in a band. Some songs are fast and some are slow.

It's best when they play a song everyone knows. Then the crowd can sing along!

Can you sing or play a musical instrument? Singing and playing music are wonderful talents so try not to be shy, stand up and show everyone your fantastic abilities.

Owl says, "Don't be shy, singing to a crowd is a real hoot!"

The pets love to put on shows so they can share their talents with everyone!

Watch as these trapeze artists swing from bar to bar. They do amazing twists and flips and they make a great team.

Trapeze artists are usually found at the circus, flying high above the crowd. It's an amazing talent that takes years of practice to make it look smooth and graceful.

Monkey says, "Swinging on vines helps me practise for the trapeze, after plenty of trying I can now do it with ease!"

You may be naturally talented at something but to bring out the best of your skills, practising makes perfect!

Skateboarders move like lightning!
They can do awesome jumps and
crazy tricks.
Polar Puppy likes to whoosh up as
high on the ramp as he can.
"I always wear a helmet so it
doesn't matter if I fall off!" says
Polar Puppy.
Roller skaters are fast, too.
"Check out my perfect figure of
eight!" says Hamster.

Do you love to go fast?
It takes a lot of skill to
balance on small wheels but
the feeling of speed and the
thrill of spinning make it all
worthwhile.
Using your feet instead of
wheels can make you just
as talented!

Bunny loves to dance no
matter where she is.
"Whenever I hear music,
I can't help but move my
feet in time to the beat,"
says Bunny.
The more she dances the
more her talent improves!
There's nothing frog likes
more than to jump which
is why skipping is his best
talent. He could jump all
day with his friends. All
they need is a rope and
never-ending energy!
Skipping is a fun talent
that you can share with
your friends.

Magician's can do almost anything. They use tricks and performing techniques to make the audience believe they are magical.

They can make things disappear and reappear and even float in the air!

Bunny can pull a carrot from a magician's hat! But watch out Bunny, sometimes other magician pets can make bunnies disappear!

Iguana's talent is one of the cleverest by far.

His natural skill is to make his body blend in with the colours and background of wherever he is. This makes him look invisible!

"Now you see me... Now you don't!" exclaims Iguana.

It's great fun to get together with friends and combine your talents!

Panda's an expert break-dancer. He can spin and twist his body in time to the music whilst balancing carefully on one arm!

To make this look really good though, Panda can't do it on his own. He needs fast music to really rock the place.

Turtle's talent is rapping in time to the music. Put this together with Panda's dancing and the talented show really comes to life!

"Hey everyone step up to the beat, as Panda moves his funky feet, he's quick and slick as he spins to the groove, now clap along as you watch him move," raps Turtle in perfect rhyme.

Tightrope walking can be tricky. The long bar helps Squirrel to balance as she edges along the tiny rope high up in the air. "Don't look down!" she reminds herself as she carefully shuffles along. Tightrope walking is another special skill usually seen at the circus. It takes a lot of practice to balance this carefully and safely high up. If you want to learn this talent, try practising nearer the ground first and always use a net on some soft cushions to catch you when you fall!

Unicycles are the trickiest kind of bike to ride. With only one wheel and no handlebars, balance is the key!
It takes a long time to learn and may not be easy but it's so much fun!
"Once you get the knack, you never look back," says Blue Bird.
Horse's talent is one you may have tried yourself.

Hula-hooping is her favourite kind of fun and she is truly talented at it.
With the right amount of spin and swing she can keep the hula hoop moving around her hips for hours, without it falling to the ground!
"Everyone can hula hoop," says Horse. "It just takes a bit of practice to get it right!"

Would you like to be in the circus?
Mouse and Dog like to pretend they are and hope one day to show their talents off in the big top!
Balancing on stilts is very tricky to perfect but Mouse really does have a talent for it. Perhaps it's because he's so little and light that he doesn't wobble too much and give us all a fright!
Mouse loves the view from way up there. His head is almost in the sky!
Clowns are the funniest performers at the circus and it takes a special pet to be good at this talent.
Dog is a talented clown and knows just what to do to make you giggle. He can make anything into something silly.
Which is the funniest? His nose, his shoes or his big colourful hair?

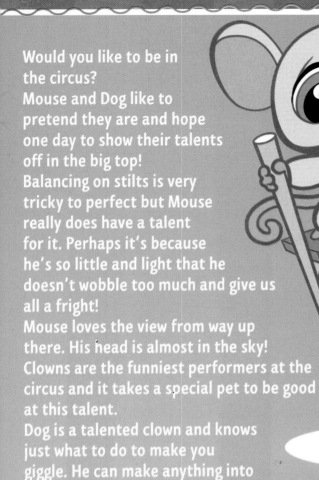

Gymnastics is a talent you can learn from very young. Be it forward rolls or handstands, it takes skill and talent to make it look good.
Beagle's best gymnastic talent is doing outrageous back flips! He loves to throw himself in the air and twist his whole body over before he lands upright on his feet.
"Watch out though, it can make you dizzy!" says Beagle.

Yo-yos spin up, down and around and around. Hermit Crab has learned to do more than throw his Yo-Yo up and down. He's so talented at this skill, he can walk it along the ground or twirl it up in the air and around his head!

"Rhythm is the key to not getting your string tangled," says Hermit Crab.

Watch the Yo-yo spin way up into the air and then back down into his hand. What a cool trick and a brilliant talent!

Ready, set, blow! It's fun to make balloons into animal shapes!

Iguana is a very talented pet. Not only can he disappear but at parties he loves to blow up balloons and twist them into crazy pet shapes for his friends.

It's a clever talent but also makes a great present for friends to take home at the end of a party.

"Can you tell what this animal shape is?" asks Iguana.

Ballet dancing is a beautiful talent to watch and enjoy. It takes hours of practice and careful strength to make this dancing look graceful. Bunny dances smoothly and softly, and she looks so pretty in pink.

"I love to twirl in my tu-tu and balance on my toes," says Bunny.

Tap-dancing is another form of dance which takes a lot of skill to make it look and sound perfect.

It's more jazzy and loud and quick, making you snap your fingers and tap along in the crowd.

Bird loves the noise her feet make as she taps along to the music.

Clickety–click-clack! Cloppety clop click!

Tap-dancing is a fun talent that lets you make a lot of loud noise!

Which talent did you like the
most? Juggling or maybe magic tricks?
Why not have a go at
something fun and skilled?
It could be as simple as banging a
drum or riding a bike. Just have a go!
Remember the more you practise the better
you'll become at your special talent.
You never know you might find you
have a real talent for it!

Every pet has a talent and every talent is
different. That's what makes us unique.
The Littlest Pet Shop Pets love to perform
and show off their talents, so let them
play and watch what they can do!
We hope you enjoyed the show!

SUMMERTIME PALS

"Can I have one of your treats?"

BUNNY

Eye Colour: Aquamarine
Body Colour: White
Age: 3
Birthday: 10th May
Favourite Accessory:
Pink flower

Loves:
Frolicking in vegtable patches
Pet Peeve: Good luck charms
Favourite Food: Carrot soup
Best Friend: Guinea Pig

Bunny's a cheeky little one, she loves nothing more than munching and jumping in the sun!

GUINEA PIG

Eye Colour: Dark blue
Body Colour:
Golden brown and white
Age: 3
Birthday: 22nd November
Favourite Accessory:
Jar filled with treats

Loves: Eating
Pet Peeve: Bellyaches
Favourite Food:
Banana bread
Best Friend: Bunny

Guinea pig loves to munch on food, there's rarely a day when he's not in the mood!

"Want a cuddle?"

CAT

Eye Colour: Pale green
Body Colour: Orange striped
Age: 4
Birthday: 29th August
Favourite Accessory:
Binoculars

Loves: Bird-watching
Pet Peeve: Cat fights
Favourite Food: Spaghetti
Best Friend: Bird

Cat's a friend to everyone, no matter who, bar none!

"Can't we all just get along?"

BIRD

Eye Colour: Dark blue
Body Colour: Pale pink
Age: 2
Birthday: 5th October
Favourite Accessory:
Swing

Loves:
Trapeze artists at the circus
Pet Peeve: Brussel sprouts
Favourite Food: Green salad
Best Friend: Cat

When the sun is out Bird will fly, to find him you'll have to look high in the sky!

"Why walk when you can fly?"

Whether it's the park or the pool, these pets love to be out in the sunshine, so head outdoors and enjoy the lazy days of summer together.

"Things are looking up!"

CHICK

Eye Colour: Light blue
Body Colour: Yellow
Age: 3
Birthday: 7th April
Favourite Accessory:
Purple basket

Loves: Hatching ideas
Pet Peeve:
Heavy metal music
Favourite Food: Muffins
Best Friend: Mouse

When Chick is about she's always on a mission to cheer everyone up and keep her sunny disposition!

MOUSE

Eye Colour: Light purple
Body Colour: White
Age: 2
Birthday: 4th June
Favourite Accessory:
Digital camera

Loves:
Snapping pictures of friends
Pet Peeve: Painting
Favourite Food:
Cheese on toast
Best Friend: Chick

Mouse loves to make you smile and laugh, so he can take your photograph!

"Say 'cheese'!"

"Pucker up!"

FROG

Eye Colour: Orange
Body Colour:
Green and yellow
Age: 5
Birthday: 13th August
Favourite Accessory:
Crown

Loves: Kissing princesses
Pet Peeve: Warts
Favourite Food:
Chips and ketchup
Best Friend: Bunny

Frog is always trying to persuade and convince, that he is really a bold and handsome prince!

BUNNY

Eye Colour: Light blue
Body Colour:
White and grey
Age: 4
Birthday: 16th July
Favourite Accessory:
Bubble-gum flavoured lip gloss

Loves: Hopscotch
Pet Peeve: Fences
Favourite Food:
Strawberries and cream
Best Friend: Frog

Of all the pets in the shop, Bunny loves sweets that make him jump and hop!

"I've got such a sweet tooth"

SUMMERTIME PALS

"I'm feeling ducky?"

DUCK

Eye Colour: Light green
Body Colour: Yellow
Age: 3
Birthday: 17th April
Favourite Accessory: Goggles

Loves: Doing backstroke
Pet Peeve: Getting out of the water
Favourite Food: Fish sticks
Best Friend: Hamster

Duck's most at home when he can play and swim, no one's as good at duck-diving as him!

CAT

Eye Colour: Bright green
Body Colour: White with grey stripes
Age: 2
Birthday: 6th September
Favourite Accessory: Running shoes

Loves: Marathons
Pet Peeve: Golf
Favourite Food: Energy drinks
Best Friend: Long Haired Cat

Guinea pig loves to munch on food, there's rarely a day when he's not in the mood!

"Wanna go for a run?"

"Striiike!"

HAMSTER

Eye Colour: Light blue
Body Colour: Golden and white
Age: 2
Birthday: 8th March
Favourite Accessory: Hamster ball

Loves: Bowling
Pet Peeve: Hitting the gutter
Favourite Food: Hot dogs
Best Friend: Duck

Hamster loves to go for a bowl, he's skilled and quick at making the ball roll!

LONG HAIRED CAT

Eye Colour: Yellow-green
Body Colour: Black and white
Age: 3
Birthday: 11th july
Favourite Accessory: Box of tissues

Loves: Sad films
Pet Peeve: Comedies
Favourite Food: Popcorn
Best Friend: Cat

Long Haired Cat just loves to weep as he curls on the sofa watching a film before sleep!

"Who's up for a film?"

"Who wants to play truth or dare?"

BEAGLE

Eye Colour: Apple green
Body Colour: Dark chocolate brown
Age: 4
Birthday: 28th May
Favourite Accessory: Bunny slippers

Loves: Flannel pyjamas
Pet Peeve: Snoring
Favourite Food: Pizza
Best Friend: Bunny

Beagle loves to play a good game, like go fish or guess the name!

SHORT HAIRED CAT

Eye Colour: Crystal blue
Body Colour: White
Age: 3
Birthday: 24th June
Favourite Accessory: Diary

Loves: Writing poems
Pet Peeve: TV
Favourite Food: Mint choc chip ice cream
Best Friend: Cat

If Short Haired Cat runs out of ink, before she can write, she'll sit and think!

"My pen is out of ink again!"

"Let's go to the games arcade!"

BUNNY

Eye Colour: Baby blue
Body Colour: White and grey
Age: 5
Birthday: 5th February
Favourite Accessory: Laptop computer

Loves: To push buttons
Pet Peeve: Computer crashes
Favourite Food: Crisps
Best Friend: Beagle

Bunny's an absolute computer nut, be it games or internet his PC's never shut!

CAT

Eye Colour: Green-brown
Body Colour: Golden
Age: 3
Birthday: 7th August
Favourite Accessory: Teddy bear

Loves: Staying up late
Pet Peeve: Ghost stories
Favourite Food: Cheesecake
Best Friend: Short haired cat

Cat's a real night-time lover, she adores watching the moon rise up above her!

"Wanna have a midnight feast?"

WINTER PETS

"Let's build a snowman!"

POLAR PUPPIES

Eye Colour: Light blue
Body Colour: Grey and white
Age: 2
Birthday: 28th December
Favourite Accessory: Snow sledge

Loves: Igloos
Pet Peeve: Summertime
Favourite Food: Any ice cream
Best Friend: Polar Puppies

The Polar Puppies can't get enough ice and snow, with their chilly noses and their mittens on, non-stop snowballs they'll throw!

POLAR PUPPIES

Eye Colour: Light blue
Body Colour: Grey and white
Age: 2
Birthday: 28th December
Favourite Accessory: Striped scarf

Loves: Icicles
Pet Peeve: Melting ice
Favourite Food: Frozen banana
Best Friend: Polar Puppies

"You call this cold"?

"Look out! Snowball fight!"

POLAR PUPPIES

Eye Colour: B aby blue
Body Colour: Brown and white
Age: 2
Birthday: 1st January
Favourite Accessory: Snowballs

Loves: Ice fishing
Pet Peeve: Not leading the pack
Favourite Food: Cherry popsicles
Best Friend: Polar Puppies

When it's snowing outside, the winter pets can't wait to throw snowballs and build snowmen, so wrap up warm and don't be afraid of the cold!

ST.BERNARD

Eye Colour: Ocean blue
Body Colour: Honey brown and white
Age: 3
Birthday: 3rd February
Favourite Accessory: Earmuffs

Loves: Snuggling
Pet Peeve: Getting lost
Favourite Food: Hot cakes
Best Friend: Bunny

St. Bernard's a real hero through and through, if you get stuck in the snow he'll rescue you!

"I'll rescue you if you fall!"

CAT

Eye Colour: Sky blue
Body Colour: Grey and white
Age: 4
Birthday: 10th January
Favourite Accessory: Sledge

Loves: Ice skating
Pet Peeve: Cold paws
Favourite Food: Frozen ice sticks
Best Friend: St. Bernard

Cat gets so excited about being in the frost, but always somehow one mitten gets lost!

"Have you seen my other mitten?"

BUNNY

Eye Colour: Artic blue
Body Colour: Golden and white
Age: 3
Birthday: 15th December
Favourite Accessory: Mittens

Loves: Being wrapped up warm
Pet Peeve: Slipping on ice
Favourite Food: Fruit smoothies
Best Friend: Cat

Bunny loves it to be snowy and chilly, but he won't play without his mittens, that would be silly!

"Who wants to build a snow bunny?"

TOTALLY TALENTED PETS
WORD SEARCH

The Littlest Pet Shop pets are a talented bunch bursting with skills! Can you find the talents and skills listed below? The words may read forwards or backwards, up or down.

```
K T I G H T R O P E
C A V N U K A N K Z
I P A C B M P T D Q
R D S L C R P E G X
T A C O S T I L T S
C N B W D E N H L V
I C G N I L G G U J
G I S F C L N M O P
A N X W L A I G D K
M G T Z P B E S O Y
```

TIGHTROPE ▨   MAGIC TRICK ☐
JUGGLING ▨   BALLET ☐
STILTS ☑   TAP DANCING ☐
CLOWN ▨   RAPPING ▨

COPY THE COLOURS

Use your crayons or coloured pencils to colour in the picture below. See if you can match and copy the correct colours.

ANSWERS

Page 14 – Pet Mix Up!

1. POODLE
2. BLUEBIRD
3. PUG
4. CAT
5. TURTLE
6. MOUSE

Page 15 – Crazy Maze

Page 16 – Crossword Time

```
M O N K E Y
O     I
U     T
S     T
E   D E
  B U N N Y
    C S
    K
```

```
    C   T
    A   U
H A M S T E R
O       T
R       L
S C O T T I E
E
```

Page 17 – What's the Difference?

Page 41 – Help Kitten

Page 60 – Word Search

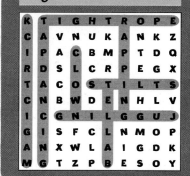